ST. MARY'S CO
LIBR

ST MARY'S COLLEGE
LIBRARY

FALLS ROAD

J/821

LEW

64444

D0236061

THE MARDI GRAS CAT

THE MARDI GRAS CAT

~ A gallery of cats in poems and pictures ~

paintings by PAUL STAGG

poems by NAOMI LEWIS

HEINEMANN · LONDON

64444

First published in Great Britain 1993
by William Heinemann Ltd
an imprint of Reed Consumer Books Limited
Michelin House, 81 Fulham road, London SW3 6RB
and Auckland, Melbourne, Singapore and Toronto

Text copyright © Naomi Lewis 1993
Illustrations copyright © Stephanie Hoppen 1993
ISBN 0 434 96051 9

Produced by Mandarin Offset
Printed and bound in China

Illustrations published by arrangement with Stephanie Hoppen

CONTENTS

THE SHIP'S CAT

Around the Horn when I was born
All stormy was the ocean-O.
Since then on land I cannot stand –
I miss the rocking motion-O.

Way, haul away,
Meow, meow, meow, meow!
Way, haul away
Meow, meow, meow.

I lost my mother at the port,
She'd gone to join a schooner-O.
But I remember all she'd taught
And how to join the shanty-O:

Way, haul away,
Meow, meow, meow, meow!
Way, haul away
Meow, meow, meow.

They sent me up the tall top-mast
To prove I was a sailor true.
They cried, "Avast!" I raced up fast
To chanting from the crew, the crew:

Way, haul away,
Meow, meow, meow, meow!
Way, haul away
Meow, meow, meow.

But at the top I chose to stop.
A cat does not climb down you know
The cabin boy was sent aloft.
But that's another shanty-O:

Way, haul away,
Meow, meow, meow, meow!
Way, haul away
Meow, meow, meow.

THE VENICE CAT

At the hour that has no name,
When the revellers are gone
And day-toilers stir in dream,
Venice then becomes our own.
Secrets lie in every stone.

See this mask? What might it tell?
When the music lost its art,
When the dawning said: "Depart" –
Did the face, when this thing fell,
Maskless, win or lose the heart?
Masks I scorn; the need is none.
Mask and face for cats are one.

Sheltered by no house, no door,
I, both hungry friar and Doge,
Live by alms, but bend no paw.
The giver has the privilege,
Am I not a symbol more
Than the lion of St Mark,
The dragon of St Theodore?

So begins another day.
The gondolas lie still below
Soon I'll hear the voices say:
"Vivaldi lived here, did you know?
When? Oh, three hundred years ago."

Now the campanile bell
Sounds, and inescapably
Both rank and salt I sense the smell
Of water-roads that meet the sea.

THE DUTCH CAT

Cornelius, I. This mansion here
I share with Mistress and Mynheer.
Some call me Poes (which you spell Puss).
To you I am Cornelius.

My twin Erasmus ornaments
The Burgomaster's residence.
So proud our mien that not a mouse
Dare venture into either house.

How is it that my sister's child
Hieronymus, can be so wild?
By the canal his days are spent
With rascals of like temperament.

True, water is Holland's element.
Though for myself I still prefer
An ordered Dutch interior.

A noble land! Yet one complaint
You must allow. It touches paint.

The great Dutch masters I revere,
Of course; Franz Hals, Van Dyck, Vermeer –
Yet where in all their canvases
Can I discern my ancestors?

Observe the Arnolfini house
(So grave and seemly, spouse and spouse);
A cat would make the scene complete.
But *Tray* wags at the master's feet.

Ah! Now at last I can record,
This failure is to be restored.
A painting's planned; I sit (or stand)
For all cats in the Netherland.

A frame of tiles I shall request;
Some tulips also, I suggest.
So clean and fine; who'd choose the rose?

The painter comes. I take my pose.

THE EGYPTIAN CAT

This is my world, sun, sand and stone.
A different scene? There can be none!
The Nile, the palms, the brilliant sky –
And at its heart, the Sphinx and I.

The goddess Nut, who rules the light
Directs the move from day to night
For me – since am I not, indeed,
The sacred creature of her creed?

The Sphinx (take pictures if you will)
Looks wise, says nothing. That's her skill.
And so she keeps her mystery still.

Ah, nothing secret can be hid
From one who watched as Cheops bid
The building of the pyramid.

At last the great tomb pierced the sky.
But stone left idle vexed the eye.
"Take it," said Chephren, Cheops' son,
"To make a Sphinx." And this was done.

Ask *me* your questions. Watch me well.
I know the answers. One day I will tell.

THE BALLET CAT

I am Ninette, a Russian Blue.
I live with dancers: I dance too.
About this I must be discreet
So few observe my dancer's feet.

Ah, but at midnight! You would say
The stage is empty, silent grey.
Not so! Each night they come in hosts,
The great immortal dancers' ghosts
Who, on these boards, once made their mark
And now bring radiance to the dark –
Karsavina and Balanchine,
Riabouchinska and Lichine …
All greatly play their greatest part
In turn – but with unearthly art.
Nijinsky leaps with casual care
And stays unmoving in the air.

Strange that the humans should be deaf
To what I hear: Prokoviev,
Delibes, Stravinsky, Weber – more,
Played now as never played before.

And I too dance: Odile, Odette,
I am Giselle. I'm Juliet.
I am the Spectre of the Rose.
The ghosts applaud, for each one knows
That none can outmatch my
entrechat, pas de chat,
jeté, fouetté,
glissade, pirouette.

Morning comes: I take a rest
Here in my private den, my nest,
I drowse, I dream …
I hear a scream –

"Again! My workbox! Out you get!"
"Yours, Madame? I much regret –
Well, move I might, but not quite yet –
Shall we discuss?"
"NO, NON and NYET."
I move. But how could she forget
That none can outmatch my
entrechat, pas de chat,
jeté, fouetté,
glissade, pirouette.

THE CAMPUS CAT

I am Catullus. I share my name with a poet.
Each of us is admired and praised by scholars.
Not the least of these is my personal human.
    Worthy companion.

So many tastes unite us: leather bound volumes,
Interchange of thoughts on time and existence,
Paste of anchovy spread on a portion of crumpet –
    Still, there's one difference.

He: "One fault only has my noble Catullus.
Vintage jazz is to him so displeasing
That, at times, I am obliged to call him
    Cato the censor.

"If I play but a phrase of Dizzy Gillespie
How he laments, and leaps about like a mad thing!
Then, to placate him, I must offer him Purcell.
    He purrs in approval."

Mosca, fly-on-the-wall, has nibbled his cake crumb.
"Now I must fly," says the fly – "my daily engagement,
Ten to three, unchanging, is Deanery tea-time,
    Honey served always."

I too have tonight an appointment,
Each full moon the faculty felines assemble:
Tiberius, Pushkin, Pope, Faraday, Hobbes, Mercator,
    Gladstone et cetera.

Catherine Cookson, cat of the college kitchen
(Such a popular member!) contrives the catering.
Regular too are the ferals (who dare oppose them?)
    Beowulf and Grendel.

First, debate: then conversation and feasting.
Last, a chorus, led by our choir The Nine Mewses.
Windows fly open! Cries! They must be applauding.
    We give an encore.

THE NEW YORK CAT

Cutie is what she calls me –
My real name is more grand,
It is also rather longer:
I cost, you understand.

Mornings? It's most worth waking
When Ogden the basement cat
Slips in with Mavis the cleaner
And brings me the local chat.

"You may be a beauty, Cutie,
But you've no call to be vain –
You'd never last long on the sidewalk;
You'd be a mess in the rain."

There's Ogden for you! He's right, though,
And I don't feel any pique.
I never was one for exertion.
Yet – a strange thing happened last week.

I watched a white cloud floating;
It looked like me, in the sky!
I leapt up from my cushion –
I heard myself utter a cry …
*"Why, what's the matter with Cutie?
Is she chasing a fly?"*

Afternoons can be boring.
Excuse me while I yawn –
Mavis has left me Tib-Nibs.
I would prefer a prawn.

Best time is evening guest time.
I do what is required,
Purr, pose, promote conversation;
And wait to be admired.

*"Oh, never mind Cutie, she's dozing.
Besides, she is very discreet."*
But Ogden and I will have plenty of mews
To exchange, when next we meet.

THE PILGRIM CAT

The night is cold; the mountains high.
Light shines from the monastery.

Pilgrim cat without a name
To the monastery came.

"Pilgrim cat with travelled feet
Turn the wheel and you shall eat."

"Willingly my bowl I earn
But I need no wheel to turn.

Since possessions have I none
In myself my wheel is spun.

But in this way it shall be done:

Human fingers are not mine.
So round your wheels my steps shall twine,
Circling in unbroken line.

Where the circles cross and meet
I await, my task complete."

"Bring a mat and bring a bowl.
Bring welcome for this pilgrim soul.

This pilgrim cat is strange and wise.
Would that he'd stay beyond sunrise."

ST. MARY'S COLLEGE
FALLS ROAD, BELFAST 12.

THE MARDI GRAS CAT

Had a home and people
Where did they go?
Had a home and people
Where did they go?
Took their goods; turned the key;
Never gave a thought to me.
I was a lost thing until I met my Beau,
My black cat Beau.

"Honey, you're too pretty
To rough it on your own.
This is a fine city
But only a cat that's streetwise
Can make it here alone."

He showed me secret places
Where we kept warm and dry.
We shared a crawfish waffle
And a slice of oyster pie.

But at Mardi Gras a voice said:
"Black cat! A good luck giver!"
A hand reached out and snatched him.
They took him down the river.
That's how we got parted,
That's why I'm broken hearted.

Looked for him up Rampart
And down Dauphine.
That cat must be somewhere
In New Orleans.
Asked the Mississippi
"Is he down below?"
"Sorry girlie – like to help –
But I ain't got your Beau.
But I ain't got your Beau."

Sun went down the west side
Sky was smoky red.
Dreamed I heard him calling,
This is what he said:

"Where you got to, baby?
Been searching low and high.
Got to find you somehow,
Don't like to hear you cry.
I'm a long way from the old place.
Wish that I could fly.
But wait for me, don't wander;
I'll be there by and by.
We'll share a crawfish waffle
And a slice of oyster pie."

Will he come at sunrise?
Will he come at noon?
Black Beau, come soon.

THE CHINESE CAT

When I came to live far from the city,
Having left the Emperor's service,
Friends said: "Can it be possible?
How will you endure the solitude,
You who have known so well the life of court?"
"Solitude," I said, "was always my intention."

How comes it then that I have a companion,
Unsought, and yet in every way congenial?
A riddle you think? I will solve it.

Seven years past to this day,
Something followed my steps.
I heard thin cries: *mee mee, mee mee.*

I plucked it from the ground. It said *pr pr.*
Sixteen pins were its claws as it clung to me.
Since then it has shared my home.

Many names has this creature.
An Emperor has not more.
Wild One, Yow Yow, Keeper of Secrets,
Each day I discover another.

Together we walk to the stream.
I for its clear water,
He, perhaps, in hope of a little fish.
My robe of state hangs from a wooden peg.
It keeps the autumn wind from the cracked wall.
When nights are cold we lie beneath its covering.

The creature has learnt many words of my language.
Should I be less of a scholar than Yow Yow?
My study is now the language of the cat.

THE SCOTTISH WILDCAT

Long, long before a human hand
Felled oak and ash and elm,
Sylvestris lived with wolf and boar
Ten thousand centuries and more.
All England was our realm.

As man increased they spared no beast
Of oldest ancestry.
They razed our forests to the ground,
Spared not a single tree.
Our claim was small, but they took all
And gave us death for fee.

Only Sylvestris still remains –
Most feared, most fierce, most free.

Sylvestris wears no coat of white,
Nor a black one either.
We take our hues from root and fern,
The brown peat-water of the burn,
And earth and sand and heather.

The wolf who never hunted man
You'll seek for now in vain.
We watched unseen from thicket green
When the last wolf was slain.

The killer told the tale with pride.
It was a tale of shame.
Within the year he pined and died,
And who now knows his name?

Our road lay north; we glided forth
Through midland hills and dales.
They came with poison, gun and stakes;
Sylvestris vanished from the Lakes,
From Yorkshire and from Wales.

You will not find Sylvestris-kind
Near crowded human scene.
But you may search in Stirlingshire
Kinross and Kincardine.
Seek in Glen Cora and Glen Esk
And the rough moors between.

Woe to the land that has no wild!
How can its humans thrive?
But on bleak hill and thorny earth
That never knew a human birth,
Sylvestris will survive.

THE SPANISH CAT

Gatito, my golden creature,
You're a prince, confess!
Gato, you know all my secrets –
Yours I can but guess.
    What I ask, you answer wisely:
    Isn't that so Gatito?
Meee-yu. That means yes?
Meee-yu. That means no?

There again, those serenadings!
It's that dark-eyed boy, I know.
Melting looks and wild guitar strings –
Creature of the *barrio* –
Gypsy music, gypsy pleadings –
What should I do, Gatito?
    He looks up; I look down.
    Should I smile? Should I frown?
    Tell me, Gatito.
Meee-yu. That means yes?
Meee-yu. That means no?

My nurse Pilar used to tell me
"There's a certain orange tree.
Once a year, for one hour only –
Niña, listen carefully –
    On it grows
    A golden rose.
Find and pluck that flower," said she,
"And your wish shall granted be."

Gato, in a dream last night,
The magic tree appeared to me.
There was the rose, a point of light,
It grew, it opened, shone like fire.
In my dreaming Pilar spoke:
    "Pluck it! Make your wish," said she,
    "And you shall have your heart's desire."
Ah, Pilar, you sorceress!
My hand went out. I cried "Success!"

A cock crowed, and I woke.

The tree was there. I saw it plain!
Tell me, tell me, Gatito,
Will I have that dream again?
(Then it will not be in vain!)
Meee-yu. That means yes?
Meee-yu. That means yes?

THE CONVENT CAT

O I am a cat of piety,
Of virtue and sobriety –
Well, how could I be other
In such a saintly company
Where I abide in harmony
With all, the only brother.

When I arrived, a foundling,
A three-week orphan, mewling,
The sisters held debate
Considered their professions,
The No-ones and the Yes-ones,
But one voice fixed my fate.

" 'Tis no irregularity
'Twill be an act of charity
The thing has no possessions
And little chance of sin,
Besides – he'll have his uses,
For don't forget the mouses
Of course he must come in,"
Said Sister Catharine.

I did not need probation;
I'd found my true vocation
In saintly occupation
Within this citadel.
A cat is always punctual
And orderly as well.

So, long before the sunrise
I rush from cell to cell.
I meet with some ingrateness
But – no Sister need fear lateness.
Why trouble with a bell?

My sleeping needs are simple,
I rest upon a wimple –
"Oh holy saints, see that!
'Tis all a crumple crimple!
Be off, you creature, scat!"
She can't mean Brother Cat!

Friday is our fish day.
To me it is my wish day –
I wish *each day* were Friday,
So holy is this cat.
I hear a sister whisper,
"Our Thomas is no doubter
Each day he looks devouter
Whatever he is at."

Could any praise be higher?
Enough now of my history
It's time to join Refectory
Then practise for the choir
In the Magnificat.
Oh who would not aspire
To be a convent cat!